This edition published by Parragon Books Ltd in 2014

Parragon Books Ltd
Chartist House
15–17 Trim Street
Bath BA1 1HA, UK
www.parragon.com

ISBN 978-1-4723-5084-8

Printed in China

TEENAGE MUTANT NINJA™ TURTLES

STEALTH MODE

PaRRagon

Bath • New York • Cologne • Melbourne • Delhi
Hong Kong • Shenzhen • Singapore • Amsterdam

CONTENTS

MY TRUE IDENTITY   8

MY NINJA IDENTITY   9

TURTLE PROFILES   10

WE ARE THE GOOD GUYS   12

TURTLES OF JUSTICE   14

ENTER THE LAIR   15

IF YOU WERE A TURTLE   16

FIND THE MUTAGEN   18

MUTANT GENERATION   19

DR PRANKENSTEIN   20

STORY: ROBOT RAMPAGE   23

BOARD NINJAS   42

THE ART OF OBSERVATION   43

SWIFT AND SILENT   44

MY LATEST INVENTION   45

PRANK PAYBACK!   46

MASKED PROBLEM   47

HAI, SENSEI!   48

SHRED THE SHREDDER   50

SENSEI WISDOM   51

BAD GUYS   52

PIZZA THE ACTION   54

SAY WHAT?   55

NINJA DISGUISE   56

TURN YOUR ROOM INTO A LAIR   57

NATURAL BORN LEADER   58

MEAN MACHINE!   60

ANGER MANAGEMENT   61

MY TRUE IDENTITY

Write your important details here.
But be careful the Kraang don't get their tentacles on them!

STICK A PHOTO OR
DRAW A PICTURE OF
YOURSELF HERE

MY REAL NAME: _____

MY AGE: _____

WHERE I LIVE: _____

PEOPLE I LIVE WITH: _____

ANIMALS I LIVE WITH: _____

MY NINJA IDENTITY

If you move among the shadows you're going to need
a secret ninja identity.

MY NINJA NAME: _____

CREATURE I WOULD MUTATE INTO: _____

WHERE I OPERATE: _____

MY SPECIAL SKILLS: _____

DESIGN AN AWESOME NINJA MASK

DRAW A PICTURE OF YOURSELF AS A NINJA

GO TEAM!

Get to know the lean, mean, green Turtle team!

LEONARDO

NICKNAME: Leo

PERSONALITY: Hard-working and dedicated to his training. He wants to be the ideal leader to his brothers ... but it's not easy when they never do as he says!

WEAPON: Katana – double swords

SECRET FACT: Leo learns his leadership skills from Captain Ryan, a character in his favourite TV show, *Space Heroes*.

DONATELLO

NICKNAME: Donnie

PERSONALITY: Curious about how things work – and how they can be improved – Donnie is the inventor and brains of the team.

WEAPON: Bo staff, with added blade

SECRET FACT: Donnie has a crush on April ... but he doesn't manage to keep that a secret!

MICHELANGELO

NICKNAME: Mikey

PERSONALITY: Mikey loves life. Dancing, skateboarding around the streets, eating pizza, playing video games ... there's not much that doesn't get him excited!

WEAPON: Nunchucks

SECRET FACT: Mikey has named all of his toes.

RAPHAEL

NICKNAME: Raph

PERSONALITY: As tough as turtle shell, Raph is strong and always the first into a fight! But he doesn't always have time for ninja niceties like stealth and silence.

WEAPON: Sai

SECRET FACT: Raph has a pet turtle called Spike. He's probably Raph's best friend!

WE ARE THE GOOD GUYS

Teamwork is vital to the Turtles' battle to save Earth.
What do your friends bring to your team? Do they all have special
skills, like the Turtles? Or are you all just great at everything?
Make this file on your teammates to find out why you work
so well together.

FRIEND 1:

REAL NAME: _____

NINJA NAME: _____

SPECIAL SKILLS: _____

_____

_____

CREATURE HE OR SHE WOULD MUTATE INTO: _____

STICK OR DRAW A PICTURE HERE

FRIEND 2:

REAL NAME: _____

NINJA NAME: _____

SPECIAL SKILLS: _____

_____

_____

CREATURE HE OR SHE WOULD MUTATE INTO: _____

STICK OR DRAW A PICTURE HERE

FRIEND 3:

REAL NAME: _____

NINJA NAME: _____

SPECIAL SKILLS: _____

_____

_____

CREATURE HE OR SHE WOULD MUTATE INTO: _____

STICK OR DRAW A PICTURE HERE

TURTLES OF JUSTICE

Every team needs a symbol – a simple badge that your members can recognize, like the Foot Clan's square foot icon. Design a symbol for your team below.

MY TEAM'S NAME IS: _____

OUR SAYING OR MOTTO IS: _____

_____

_____

ENTER THE LAIR

Your team's going to need a lair. Somewhere you can train, devise plans, work on your latest inventions, or just kick back and shellax! The Turtles have their lair in the sewers and subway tunnels. Shredder has one, too. Even the Kraang have a secret hideout! Draw your lair here!

WHERE IS YOUR TEAM'S SECRET HIDEAWAY?

_____

_____

WHAT IS THE SECRET PASSWORD?

_____

_____

IF YOU WERE A TURTLE

... who would you be? Find out by ticking one box as your answer to each question.

How strong are you?

- [ ] A] I'M AS TOUGH AS A TURTLE SHELL!
- [ ] B] I'M STRONG IN MIND AND SPIRIT
- [ ] C] BRAINS BEAT MUSCLES ANY DAY
- [ ] D] I'M WORKING ON IT!

You're riding in the Shellraiser – would you ...

- [ ] A] MAN THE WEAPONS
- [ ] B] DRIVE
- [ ] C] BE THE CHIEF ENGINEER
- [ ] D] TELL THE DRIVER WHERE TO GO

If you're angry, what do you do?

- [ ] A] BLOW A FUSE
- [ ] B] TALK ABOUT IT
- [ ] C] GO TO YOUR ROOM
- [ ] D] EAT PIZZA

Which word best describes you?

- A] LOUD
- B] RESPONSIBLE
- C] CLEVER
- D] FRIENDLY

To relax you like to...

- A] SPEND TIME WITH YOUR PETS
- B] PLAY VIDEO GAMES
- C] BUILD THINGS
- D] PLAY PRANKS

You're surrounded by enemies, what do you do?

- A] GET BUSY BASHING THOSE BADDIES
- B] THINK OF A CLEVER PLAN TO BEAT THEM ... THEN BEAT THEM!
- C] BACK UP YOUR BROTHERS
- D] GET READY FOR SOME FUN!

MOSTLY As

You are like Raphael. You're tough, strong and hot-headed. Your friends feel safe around you, but you act before you think. This can sometimes get you into big trouble!

MOSTLY Bs

You are like Leonardo. You're a leader – smart, thoughtful and responsible. You're always there for your friends, but you should sometimes listen to them more.

MOSTLY Cs

You are like Donatello. You're super clever and your friends look up to you because you always have the answers. You're a great team member, but you need to work on building your confidence.

MOSTLY Ds

You are like Michelangelo. You're friendly, energetic and fun-loving. You're the joker among your friends and you make them laugh, but you don't always think things through.

FIND THE MUTAGEN

There are 10 canisters of mutagen hidden in this picture.
Colour them in as you find them. Then colour in the whole scene.

JOKE CORNER

LEO HAS A PLAN TO CLEAN ALL OF NEW YORK'S SEWERS...

BUT IT'S REALLY JUST A PIPE DREAM!

Answer:

MUTANT GENERATION

What was the last plant or animal you touched?
If you were hit with mutagen right now, that's the creature you
would mutate into. Draw yourself as a mutant hybrid below!

MIKEY LOVES TO NAME THINGS: CHRIS BRADFORD
BECAME DOGPOUND, SNAKE BECAME SNAKEWEED ...
WHAT WOULD HE CALL YOUR MUTANT CREATURE?

DR PRANKENSTEIN

Mikey is the king of practical jokes – most of them involve water balloons and an angry Raphael! Come up with some of your own!

HERE'S A FEW TO GET YOU STARTED:

Carefully unroll part of a roll of toilet paper. Write something silly on one of the sheets, like "Help me! I'm trapped in a toilet paper factory!", or just "Boo!", Then carefully roll it back up again. The person who finds it will wonder what's going on!

Put one or two small white sweets in your mouth. Pretend to fall over, and spit out the sweets – for a second, everyone will think it's your teeth!

Squash a raisin in a piece of paper. Show it to your friends, telling them you just squashed a fly ... then eat it.

WHAT'S THE JOKE? _____
_____
_____

WHEN I WILL PLAY IT _____
_____
_____

WHAT'S THE JOKE? _____
_____
_____

WHEN I WILL PLAY IT _____
_____
_____

WHAT'S THE JOKE? _____
_____
_____

WHEN I WILL PLAY IT _____
_____
_____

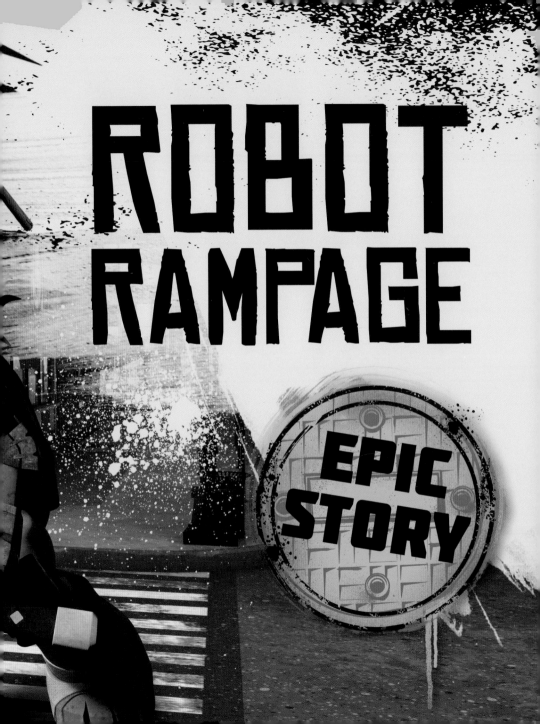

It was late at night and the Teenage Mutant Ninja Turtles were in an abandoned warehouse, battling their enemies, the Kraang!

The Kraang were blobby, weird-looking pink brains – and they used robots called Kraangdroids to carry them around and fight their battles.

SMASH! Raphael knocked out a Kraangdroid and a pink Kraang jumped out of it and scurried away.

SLAM! Donatello tried to use his wooden bo staff against another robot, but it bounced off! The robot wasn't hurt. "Are you kidding me?" Donatello cried.

The Kraang fired a laser blast at the Turtles. Raph held up his sai and the blast bounced off the metal, but when the laser reached Donatello, it blew his wooden staff to pieces!

"Dude, your weapon just exploded!" Mikey said.

"Donnie, take cover!" Leonardo ordered. Leo had a plan to stop the Kraang attacking. He threw a ninja star, hit a lever inside a forklift and sent the vehicle ploughing into the robots.

The Turtles were safe – for now.

At the end of the battle Donatello recovered an empty Kraang robot.

"Hey, guys, give me a hand with this," he said.

"What do you want that thing for?" Raphael asked.

"Don't you want to understand how these things work?" Donnie was fascinated by the advanced technology of the Kraang so they helped him carry the robot back to the lair.

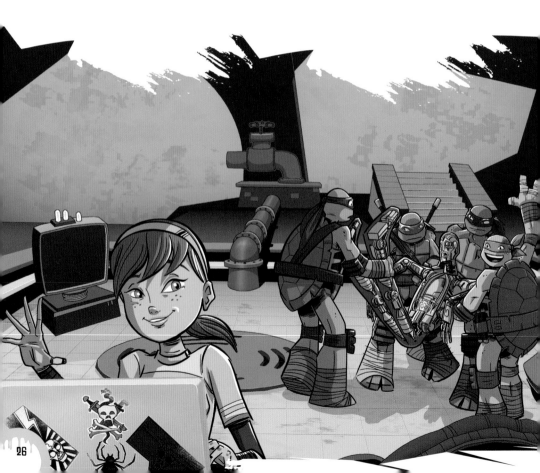

When they got there, Splinter gave Donatello a new bo staff. "I can't keep fighting with this," Donatello told Splinter. "I want to use modern technology."

"You may upgrade your weapon," Splinter said, "but remember, combat is not a video game."

Donatello thought for a moment. "That's it! I'll turn combat into a video game!"

Splinter shook his head as Donnie dragged the robot into his lab.

The next day, April showed them a website she had made, where people could post messages about strange things they saw around the city. Someone had posted a video about a gas explosion in the warehouse district. April pressed pause. They could see a Kraangdroid in the background!

"We'll check it out tonight," Leonardo said. "We can't go out in the daytime." Splinter didn't want people to see the Turtles.

"Well, I can," April said, and she went to investigate.

In the warehouse district, April spotted some Kraangdroids.
She hid and overheard an evil plan.

"The mutagen will be tomorrow unleashing in the water
supply that supplies the humans' supply of water," one said.
Mutagen was the radioactive ooze that had turned the Turtles
into mutants – if it was in the water, thousands of people would
mutate as well! April gasped. She had to tell the Turtles!

Meanwhile, back at the lair, Donatello had used the technology from the captured Kraang robot in his new weapon – a robot who could fight like a ninja!

Donnie stepped forward, holding a video-game controller. "Gentlemen, this is the future!" he said.

"I always thought the future would be taller," Raph said.

"It can do all the dangerous stuff while we stay safe," said Donnie.

"So it's for wimps," Raph said.

"Try it," Donnie said, "attack him!"

Raph, Leo and Mikey all attacked, but they couldn't make a dent!

"Let's call it Metalhead!" said Mikey.

It was now dark outside, so Mikey, Raph and Leo went out into the city. They leaped across rooftops and waited on a ledge.

CLANG! CLANG! CLANG! Metalhead slowly caught up with them. Donnie was back in the lair, controlling the robot like a video game.

April caught up with the Turtles on her way back from the warehouse. She gasped when she saw Metalhead.

The Turtles explained about Donnie's invention and she waved her hand impatiently. "Listen, we have to do something," she said.

"The Kraang are going to poison the city's water supply with mutagen!" She quickly led them back to the Kraang's warehouse.

Outside, April and Metalhead waited behind while Leo, Mikey and Raph sneaked up on the Kraang inside. The Turtles lurked in the dark, watching the Kraangdroids load mutagen onto trucks. Then, on Leo's command, they ran over and attacked!

"HIIII-YAH!" Raph shouted.

Meanwhile, April and Metalhead were watching the building when an energy blast suddenly shot through the roof!

They heard Michelangelo shout: "They're everywhere! Run!"

It sounded like the three Turtles had been cornered by the Kraang. Donnie, who was watching the action through Metalhead's eyes, knew he had to help!

Suddenly, Metalhead crashed through the roof and landed in the middle of the action. The Turtles and the Kraang all stopped fighting and stared.

"Why are you standing like that?" Leonardo asked. Metalhead's arms were in a weird position.

"Don't I look heroic?" Metalhead said in Donatello's voice.

"No!" Leonardo shouted.

"Sorry," Metalhead said. "Wrong button!"

The battle continued. Metalhead really did seem invincible! Donatello watched from the lair, excited. He made Metalhead move faster and faster, blasting lasers all over the place.

Finally, he found his target....

BOOM! The Kraang's pile of mutagen exploded.

The city's water supply was safe, but Metalhead was damaged in the explosion.

Donnie lost contact with the robot. "Guys, if you can hear me, run!" he shouted.

Suddenly, a Kraang jumped out of its damaged droid body and onto Metalhead. The robot's eyes glowed red. Now the Kraang was controlling him!

Evil Metalhead attacked the Turtles.

Back at the lair, Donnie grabbed his bo staff. "It's time to stop playing games," he said, and ran straight to the warehouse. He took on Evil Metalhead while the other Turtles fought the Kraang.

Donnie dodged attack after attack from his own robot, until one powerful laser blast broke his staff in two. "Not again!" he shouted. But then he spotted a loose beam on the ceiling and positioned himself under it.

"Come and get me!" Donnie called out to Evil Metalhead. Evil Metalhead sent out one more laser blast. At the last second, Donnie jumped aside and the laser hit the loose beam. As it came crashing down, it fell onto the robot!

Gears crunched and sparks crackled as Donnie stabbed Evil Metalhead with his broken staff. The robot was defeated! The Kraang jumped off and scurried away.

"Awesome!" Donatello shouted.

After defeating the last few Kraang, Michelangelo and Leonardo patted Donnie's back.

"Nice job, bro!" Mikey said.

Donnie was proud of himself.

"Not bad," Raphael said. "Except for the part where you got us into this mess in the first place...."

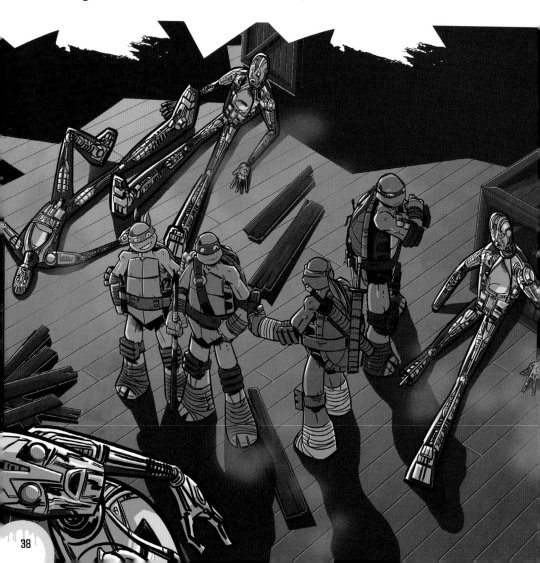

Later, back in the lair, Donatello began to work on a new project. Splinter thought he looked sad.

"What troubles you?" Splinter asked.

"This was all my fault," Donatello said.

"Yes, you are responsible," Splinter replied. "But you are also responsible for saving the city."

Donnie felt better. "In the end," he said, "there was nothing better than a wooden stick ... "

" ... except a laser-guided wooden stick!" Donatello held up the new weapon he was working on. Then he slammed it against the ground and it started to make a strange sound.

"It's not supposed to do that!" Donatello cried. **"RUN!"**

BOARD NINJAS

Colour in these skateboarding ninja heroes!

THE ART OF OBSERVATION

Some people can't see what is right in front of them.
Test your ninja skills by finding these words in the grid.
Look forwards, backwards, up, down and diagonally.

DOJO   HAJIME   HERO   JUSTICE
NINJA   POWER   SENSEI   SHADOW
STEALTH   SWORD

```
E  M  E  N  S  T  O  Q  Q  H
O  M  C  I  Y  H  R  J  T  H
R  X  I  N  X  P  A  L  O  I
E  T  T  J  V  Z  A  D  V  D
H  J  S  A  A  E  X  D  O  Q
K  K  U  Y  T  H  O  X  P  W
I  H  J  S  K  S  H  O  C  R
S  E  N  S  E  I  W  N  E  U
D  R  O  W  S  E  R  K  Z  I
I  T  I  F  R  C  Q  J  D  N
```

SWIFT AND SILENT

Here's a game to hone your ninja skills with some friends. The only things you need are a blindfold and an empty room in which to play.

1 One of you must be the masked ninja. The masked ninja stands in the centre of the room, wearing the blindfold.

2 Everybody else starts at one end of the room. Without running, everyone must try to reach the other end of the room without the masked ninja touching them.

3 The masked ninja can move around as much as they like to try to tag the others as they attempt to sneak past.

4 Once everyone reaches the other end of the room, head back the other way. Whoever is tagged is out of this round.

5 Whoever is the last person to be tagged is the ninja master! That person gets the blindfold for the next round.

MY LATEST INVENTION

Donnie loves making high-tech tools out of old junk – from the tPod for playing music to the Stealth Bike for cruising round the city and chasing the Foot Clan! What epic ninja invention would you come up with? A new weapon to take down your enemies? A rocket-powered skateboard? A mobile pizza-maker? Draw and describe your creation below!

PRANK PAYBACK!

Mikey has pranked his brothers once too often and now it's payback time! They each fling a water balloon at him – but which Turtle scores a direct hit?

Answer: Leonardo

MASKED PROBLEM

Looks like it's time to fight some crime, but the Turtles need to make sure they have their masks on before they leave the lair. Can you sort out the masks so there is only one of each colour in each column, row and mini square?

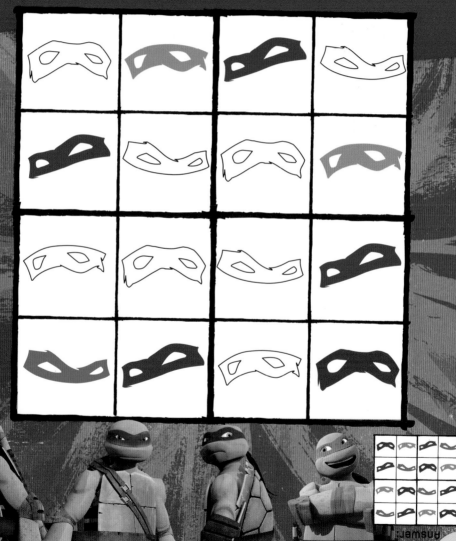

Answer:

HAI, SENSEI!

Ninjas need to be smart and dedicated. Fill in your favourite things about school on these pages.

THE SUBJECT I AM BEST AT IS ... _____

BECAUSE ... _____
_____

MY FAVOURITE SUBJECT IS ... _____

BECAUSE ... _____
_____

MY LEAST FAVOURITE SUBJECT IS ... _____

BECAUSE ... _____
_____

MY FAVOURITE TEACHER IS ... _____

BECAUSE ... _____
_____
_____

WHEN I AM OLDER I WANT TO BE ... _____

BECAUSE ... _____
_____
_____
_____
_____
_____
_____
_____
_____
_____
_____

MY DREAM IS ...
_____
_____
_____
_____
_____

SHRED THE SHREDDER

It's a full-on fight between the Turtles and Shredder!
Five things have changed in the bottom picture.
Colour one ninja star each time you find a difference.

Answer:

50

SENSEI WISDOM

Which of these things would Splinter NOT say?

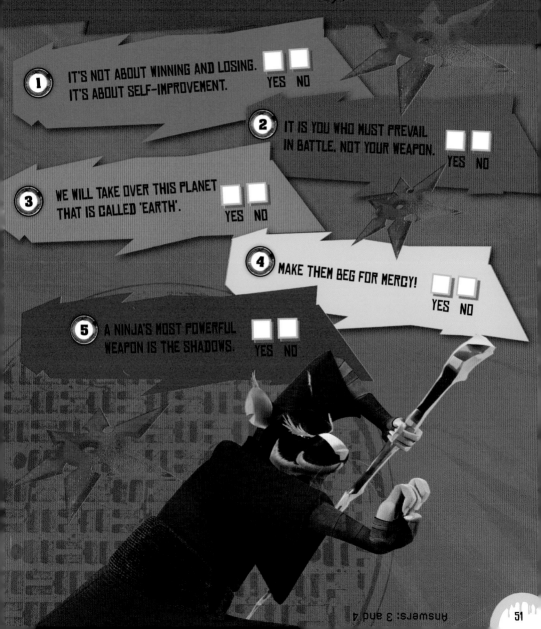

1. IT'S NOT ABOUT WINNING AND LOSING. IT'S ABOUT SELF-IMPROVEMENT.

YES   NO

2. IT IS YOU WHO MUST PREVAIL IN BATTLE, NOT YOUR WEAPON.

YES   NO

3. WE WILL TAKE OVER THIS PLANET THAT IS CALLED 'EARTH'.

YES   NO

4. MAKE THEM BEG FOR MERCY!

YES   NO

5. A NINJA'S MOST POWERFUL WEAPON IS THE SHADOWS.

YES   NO

Answers: 3 and 4

BAD GUYS

If your team is going to be Earth-saving mutant-ninja heroes, you'll have to catch the bad guys....

WHO ARE THEY? Are they a street gang, like the Purple Dragons, or a ninja clan like the Foot Clan? An alien race like the Kraang? Or a personal enemy like the evil Shredder and his assassins?

THE BAD GUYS' NAME: _____

THEY USE THESE WEAPONS: _____

_____

_____

_____

_____

DRAW YOUR BAD GUYS HERE:

HOW WILL YOU AND YOUR TEAM DEFEAT THEM?

_____

_____

_____

PIZZA THE ACTION

There's nothing Michelangelo loves more than pizza and he's not fussy about toppings. Draw your own pizza creation below. Use your favourite foods or come up with a gross new combination that only Mikey would eat!

SAY WHAT?

Finish these Turtle sayings by choosing the right word.

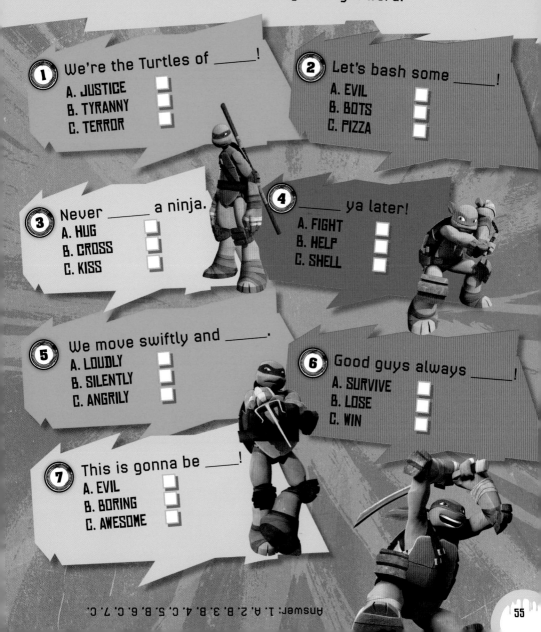

1 We're the Turtles of _____!
A. JUSTICE
B. TYRANNY
C. TERROR

2 Let's bash some _____!
A. EVIL
B. BOTS
C. PIZZA

3 Never _____ a ninja.
A. HUG
B. CROSS
C. KISS

4 _____ ya later!
A. FIGHT
B. HELP
C. SHELL

5 We move swiftly and _____.
A. LOUDLY
B. SILENTLY
C. ANGRILY

6 Good guys always _____!
A. SURVIVE
B. LOSE
C. WIN

7 This is gonna be _____!
A. EVIL
B. BORING
C. AWESOME

NINJA DISGUISE

Can you tell which Turtle is which? Colour in their masks before checking if you're right.

1

2

3

4

Answers: 1. DONATELLO, 2. MICHELANGELO, 3. RAPHAEL, 4. LEONARDO

TURN YOUR ROOM INTO A LAIR

Make a list of all the ninja gear you keep in your room —
everything you need for your stealth training and everything
you need to have an **AWESOME TIME!**

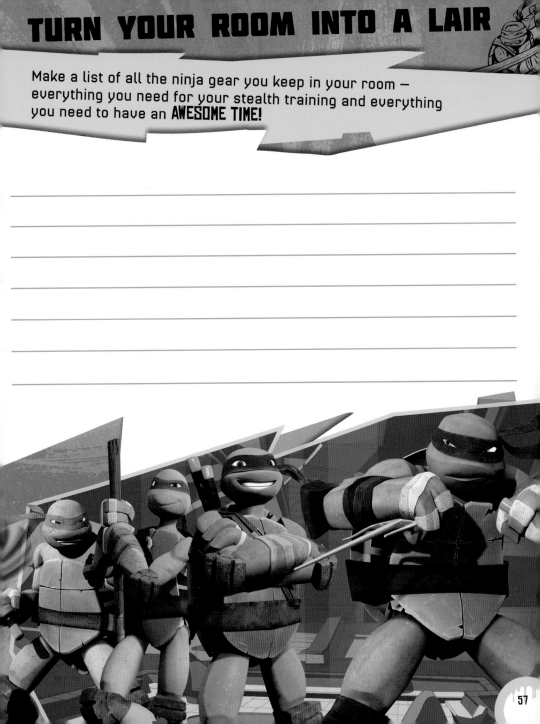

NATURAL BORN LEADER

Here's a bold and daring plan: copy this picture of Leo onto the opposite page. Use the grid lines as a guide.

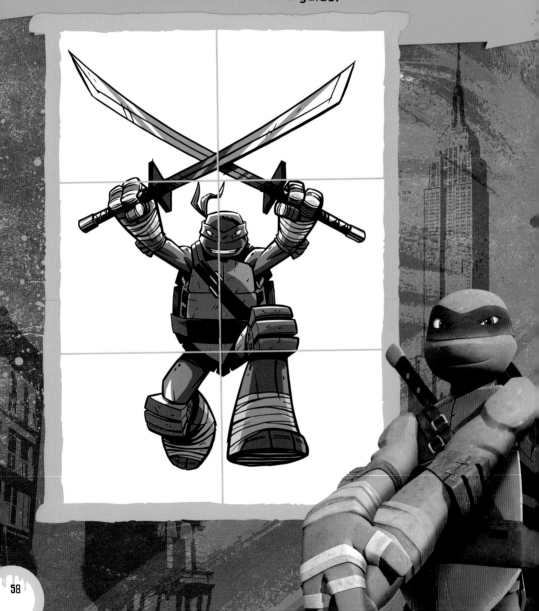

NOW ADD SOME COLOUR
TO YOUR HALF-SHELL HERO!

MEAN MACHINE!

Add some colour to Donatello's masterpiece – the Shellraiser!

ANGER MANAGEMENT

Raph accidentally smashed this picture of the Turtles during a tough training session. Draw lines to connect the shattered pieces to the correct gaps.